Nature's Hidden Adventures

SHANE CASEY

ILLUSTRATED BY
Vincent Killowry

Suitable for Dyslexic Readers

ISBN: 978-0-9927490-1-9

1 3 5 7 9 10 8 6 4 2

Published by Shane Casey
Font: OpenDyslexic – Available at http://dyslexicfonts.com

Layout and Design: Shirley Casey - SLD Design

Printing: Carlow Advertiser & Printing.

Further Information: www.shanecaseybooks.ie

This publication has been supported by Dublin City Council in recoginaton of its
contribution to biodiversity education within the City and UNESCO Dublin Bay Biosphere,
and the City's designation as a UNESCO City of Literature.

Acknowledgements:

Many thanks to all my family and friends
for their continued support and encouragement in publishing this book.

This book belongs to

....

**For my wife, Shirley,
who is Hazel to my Roland.**

The Tale of Two Hedgehogs

It was getting late on a mild July evening, when Hazel set eyes on Roland for the very first time. The sun had already bid goodnight to the day, and the moon had draped his silvery cloak across the fields of wheat and barley. Hazel was climbing over the brow of a ditch when she saw something peculiar. It was Roland, and he was doing his best to unearth a big, juicy earthworm from beneath the hedge.

Roland's eyes were shut tight, his breath was held and a tiny high-pitched squeal escaped his lips, as he pulled the earthworm with all his might. Of course, the earthworm wasn't going to give up without a fight. So it wrapped its long body tightly around the roots and stones in the ground.

Eventually though, it couldn't hold on anymore and with one last great pull from Roland, the earthworm came loose. Now, what happened next is a story that Hazel has never let Roland live down.

Roland you see, was not expecting the earthworm to come loose in that moment, and he accidently let go of it!

Well... the earthworm went flying through the air in a cloud of clay and dust.

Roland went tumbling head-over-heels backwards and ended up a dazed, dusty ball of spikes.

And Hazel simply burst out laughing. In fact, she was laughing so much that she too ended up rolling around on the ground. Which was lucky for the earthworm, as it managed to escape back down its tunnel before either Roland or Hazel could pull themselves together!

It was only when Roland was back on his feet and had given himself a good shake down, that he finally noticed Hazel for the first time. Hazel was, without a doubt, the most beautiful hedgehog he had ever seen, with deep brown eyes that were filled with mischief.

Hazel was nearly twelve weeks old. Like other young hedgehogs her own age, she had already left home and was quite capable of taking care of herself. Roland on the other hand, who was just shy of nine weeks old, was still adjusting to life on his own.

Hedgehogs, you see, are solitary animals. Once they leave home, at around eight weeks of age, they spend the rest of their lives on their own.

They snooze all day in their nest of grass and dry leaves. Then each evening as the sun fades from the day, they emerge and go about their business.

This, of course, mainly involves nosing through the undergrowth in search of scrumptious slugs, zesty spiders and crispy caterpillars for their tea.

However, each night Roland and Hazel would always make sure to meet up, and each night it would be somewhere different...

At the gap in the hedge. At the base of the old beech tree. Or even in the garden behind the farmhouse.

They would tell each other everything
they had seen and done that evening.
And when there was nothing left to say,
they would simply sit in silence and try
to count all the stars in the sky.
Then as dawn began to break across the
horizon, they would say their goodbyes
and return to their nests once again.

Summer quickly passed them by, until the leaves of the trees began to change their colours. Roland and Hazel both knew they would soon have to find somewhere to hibernate.

All hedgehogs hibernate. First, they find somewhere safe to spend the winter months. Then, they slow down their breathing and heart rate, so it appears like they're in a very deep sleep.

Needless to say, when they 'wake up', they immediately go in search of food... after all, they won't have had anything to eat for five long months!

Now, most hedgehogs hibernate alone, but sometimes a male and female will hibernate together. And that is exactly what Hazel and Roland decided to do. The only question that remained was... where?

They tried an old rabbit's burrow at the bottom of the field, but there wasn't enough space for two. They tried under the hedge, but the ground was too stony and not very comfortable. They tried under the garden shed, but the farmyard cat kept pestering them.

They tried in the compost heap, but it was very smelly in there. They tried under a pile of sticks, but it wasn't very secure.

Poor Roland and Hazel. They were fast running out of options and the weather was already turning colder. They had almost given up hope, when finally...

At the back of the hay shed, there lay an old ash tree which had fallen over many years ago during a storm. Its trunk had become hollow over time. And it was there, in the heart of that old ash tree, that Hazel and Roland found the perfect place to hibernate.

So working together, they quickly gathered leaves and moss to make it warm and comfortable. Then nestled side by side, they began to hibernate.

Thats how they stayed, snuggled warmly together as the winter storms howled outside. Until finally, the first snowdrops began to bloom, announcing the end of winter and heralding the beginning of Spring.

THE END

Senan's Story

Senan was scared.
In fact, he was terrified, and you could
hardly blame him. Indeed most young
birds are a little bit scared about flying
for the very first time. But Senan was a
swift, and he knew that a swift shouldn't
be scared of flying!

Swifts are born to fly, and spend almost their entire lives on the wing. They eat, drink and even sleep while flying.
So for a young swift like Senan to be scared to fly... well that was a very strange thing indeed.

Everyday, Senan would peer over the edge of his nest, and watch his parents twist and turn on the Summer's breeze. They were like two ballerinas dancing to some beautiful music that only they could hear.

Senan wished that he could find the courage to join them. After all, he was nearly eight weeks old, and should really have fledged his nest by now.

Each day, Senan stood at the edge of the nest and stretched out his wings like all young swifts do. But whenever he looked down, he kept imagining that he was falling towards the ground, and the ground was rushing up to meet him.

It always made him jump back in fright to the safety of the nest. What if he couldn't fly? It was a long way down, and the ground looked really hard...

You see, swifts don't
build their nests in
trees or hedges like
other birds do. They build them
on the side of tall buildings, where the
ground below isn't a soft patch of grass.
It's a hard concrete footpath!

Senan's parents had made their home in a quaint little town, where the buildings reached high up into the sky.
Their nest was on the side of one of these buildings, in a small crevice where the wall meets the roof.

The nest was made from leaves and feathers that Senan's parents had found blowing in the wind, and stuck together with their saliva. Now that might sound a bit disgusting, but it was safe, warm and comfortable. The perfect home for Senan and his two sisters.

Unfortunately for Senan's parents, however, they didn't have very many opportunities to enjoy its comforts.

From the moment they hatched
from their eggs, Senan and his two
sisters seemed to be constantly hungry.
It took every ounce of energy that their
parents had to make sure their chicks
always had plenty of food. And what
lovely food it was... crunchy aphids,
crispy midges, and chewy hoverflies.
In fact, Senan and his sisters could eat
them morning, noon and night!

Now, Senan's sisters had fledged a few days earlier, and so it was just Senan left.

His parents were very patient, but as the days passed they became more and more concerned. It would soon be time to migrate, and Senan would have to get as much flying practice as possible before leaving.

Swifts as you may know, arrive here at the beginning of Summer. Then, as the leaves on the trees begin to change into their Autumn colours, they depart again. Senan would soon have to join his parents and all the other swifts, and fly thousands of miles to South Africa.

Finally, Senan's Dad decided it was time for the two of them to have a big chat! So Senan's Dad sat at the edge of the nest, and told Senan the following story.

'When I was your age, I was scared about flying too. So was your Grandfather, and your Great-grandfather before him. In fact, every swift is scared of flying, and that's the secret to our success. When you're scared you try harder, and when you try harder you succeed'.

This was quite a shock to Senan, who always thought his Dad was the bravest swift that ever lived.

'But what if I fall?'asked Senan.

'You'll fall for a little bit', answered his Father. 'But when you open out your wings, the wind will gather around you and lift you up. And you'll fly better than any bird ever has'.

So Senan stood at the edge of the nest, took a deep breath, and jumped...

And yes, he did fall for a little bit. But just as his Father had told him, when he opened out his wings the wind gathered around him and lifted him up. Senan was flying!

Actually, he was doing more than just flying. He was twisting and turning. He was gliding and soaring. He was rolling and diving.

It seemed like every movement he made came as natural to him as breathing, and it was performed with an unparalleled grace. In fact, of all the swifts in the sky, Senan was by far the most graceful.

Needless to say, from that day on,
Senan never stopped flying.
And sometimes at the end of a long
Summer's day, if you happen to look
upwards, you might just see Senan's
sillhoutte against the evening sky.

THE END

The Life of Bombus Reilly

Bombus Reilly was a bumblebee, and a most unusual bumblebee at that! She was born and raised many years ago in an old field-mouse nest. It was in a little park that nestled into the bend of a winding river, and what a wonderful little park it was!

At its entrance, there were four beautiful old whitebeam trees. These led into an open expanse of wildflower meadows, where dasies and dandelions danced from dawn to dusk. Along its boundary, there was a string of woodland groves. They were full of hawthorn and rowan trees, that blushed each Autumn with thousands of ruby red berries.

And right at the edge of the river, with flowers matching every colour of the rainbow, was a most enchanting little marsh. There was the purple of loosestrife, the yellow of flag iris, and the blue of forget-me-nots. Indeed, for a young bumblebee like Bombus, it was like living in paradise.

Each morning, the sun would rise above the horizon, drenching the woodlands with light. Then the most beautiful choir would be heard singing. Blackbirds and bullfinches would lend their voices to the chorus, while great tits and thrushes would join in for the encore.

Then, as the morning gave way to midday, the marsh and wildflower meadows would come to life. There were dazzling dragonflies and striking shieldbugs. Hungry young frogs hopped through the marsh, while tiny pygmy shrews scuttled through the grass in search of cruchy beetles.

Of course, like any beautiful park, there were lots of people there as well. Chirdren would play in the woods and among the wild flowers of the meadow, while their parents relaxed in the sunshine.

Most of the people however, were oblivious to the busy world of the tiny creatures all around them. And there were very few creatures more busy than the bumblebees.

All bumblebees that is, except one!

Bumblebees, as you may know, have a reputation for being very busy, and there's a good reason for this.
At the beginning of each Summer, queen bumblebees lay their eggs, and every young bee that hatches is a girl! Now, usually the daughter of a queen would be considered a princess, but that's not the case for young bumblebees.

In fact, these young bees are known as workers! This is because their main role in life is to collect nectar from flowers, and return it to the bee hive to feed the queen's next clutch of young bees.

A queen has several clutches of young bees throughout the summer, and just like her first clutch, each one that hatches is a girl. Bumblebee boys are born later in the Summer!

So most of the time, young bumblebees are only ever seen hurrying from one flower to the next, collecting nectar. Bombus Reilly, however, rarely appeared to be very busy, and for a bumblebee, this was most unusual...

You see, Bombus loved nothing more than to talk to the flowers, and the flowers loved Bombus because she was so friendly. Flowers, believe it or not, have lots to say, but very few creatures take the time to listen!

So while all the other bumblebees hurried from one flower to the next, without even saying 'hello', Bombus always took her time. She would ask each and every one how their day was going.

The red clovers loved to chat, while the white clovers always had the latest gossip. But of all the flowers that Bombus visited each day, her favourite was Davin.

Davin was a most elegant dandelion, with bright yellow petals and delicate green leaves. And Davin had the most wonderful stories to tell.

Of course, listening to stories all day meant that Bombus wasn't very efficient at collecting nectar. To her sisters, it seemed that Bombus had a far too easy and carefree life. They weren't very impressed, and so they went to the queen to complain.

Queen Hannah was a beautiful bumblebee, with a golden crown on her head, and a golden sash around her waist. But what really made her stand out from the crowd, was her sandy-coloured tail!

Now, as well as being beautiful, Queen Hannah was also very wise and very fair. She would never make a judgement based on second-hand information. So she visited all the flowers herself to find out the truth about Bombus.

Every flower loved Bombus, and they pleaded with the queen to let her continue to visit them. However, it was Davin, who Queen Hannah was most interested in hearing from...

You see, Davin and Queen Hannah were old friends. This is because dandelions are one of the first nectar rich flowers to bloom each Spring, when bumblebee queens emerge from hibernation and are searching for food. And so the fate of Bombus Reilly was down to Davin.

Davin told Queen Hannah how Bombus helped to brighten up every flowers day, and the queen's heart was filled with pride.

After all, brightening up someone elses day is more important than being busy! So the queen allowed Bombus to continue to visit all the flowers, and spend as much time with them as she pleased.

Needless to say, the story of Bombus Reilly, who lived a carefree life, spread throughout the countryside. It spread first among the flowers and the trees. Then it spread among the insects, mammals and birds. The story was told and re-told, along river banks and hedgerows, in ditches and in fields.

Then one day, it was overheard by some children, who were playing hide-and-seek among the trees. Before long, the saying, 'the life of Reilly', became part of everyday language.

However, over the years the story behind the saying was forgotten.

Today only a handful of people know who Reilly really was...

and now that includes you!

THE END

A LITTLE BIT ABOUT:

HEDGEHOGS

Most baby hedgehogs are born in June. The females give birth to four or five baby hedgehogs, or urchins, which are weaned from their mother at around six weeks of age.

Hedgehogs are solitary animals, and once weaned, they spend the rest of their lives on their own.

In their first Summer it is vital that young hedgehogs reach a weight of 450g (or one pound) before they begin hibernation. This is so they have enough fat reserves to last them until Spring.

Hedgehogs are nocturnal animals, which means they sleep during the day, and are active at night. A hedgehog can travel up to three kilometres in a single night in search of food!

SWIFTS

Swifts are annual visitors to Ireland, arriving from Africa from mid-April, and returning to Africa each Autumn.

They are one of the fastest birds in Ireland, and are very distinctive when flying, with scythe shaped wings held straight out from the body.

Their feet are small and weak, so they spend almost their entire lives on the wing, landing only to build a nest. They can eat, drink, and even sleep while flying.

The nest is built in the eaves of buildings, and so the swift is commonly seen in towns and villages throughout the country.

BUMBLEBEES

Bumblebees are different to honeybees. There is only one species of honeybee in Ireland, while there are twenty different species of bumblebee.

Bumblebees are identified by the colour of their tail. The buff-tailed (sandy-coloured) bumblebee is one of the most widespread and distinctive bumblebees in Ireland.

Buff-tailed bumblebees are one of the earliest bumblebee species to emerge from hibernation each Spring. When they emerge, the queens need to quickly find lots of food, so that they can successfully begin new bumblebee colonies.

However, there are few flowers in bloom at this time of the year, and so nectar rich flowers such as dandelions are particularly important.